JANE SMISOR BASTIEN ♦ LISA BASTIEN HANSS

A DEBUT FOR YOU

TO THE PIANISTS

If you are preparing for your first performance in a special situation, then you will be making your debut. *Debut* is a French word, pronounced *day BYOO*.

Maybe you've already had your debut playing for other students of your piano teacher, but we hope you will have many more debuts in your life—perhaps playing for your class in school, or for your grandparents, or for parties.

We hope that you will love playing these pieces whether it's for a debut or not!

CONTENTS

ISBN 0-8497-9506-0

Recycling

Lisa Bastien Hanss

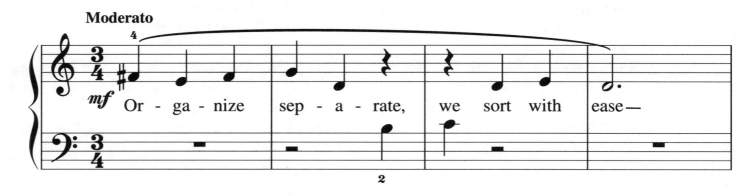

Moderato

Or - ga - nize sep - a - rate, we sort with ease—

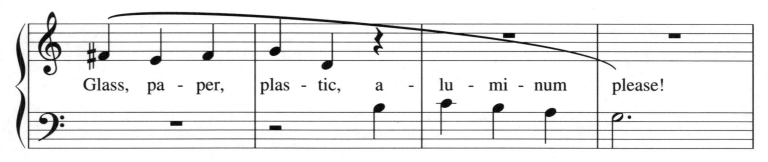

Glass, pa - per, plas - tic, a - lu - mi - num please!

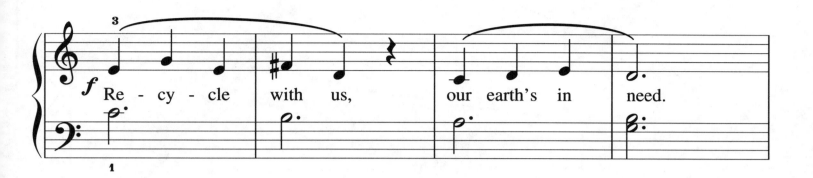

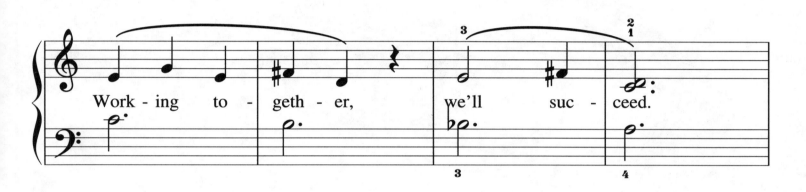

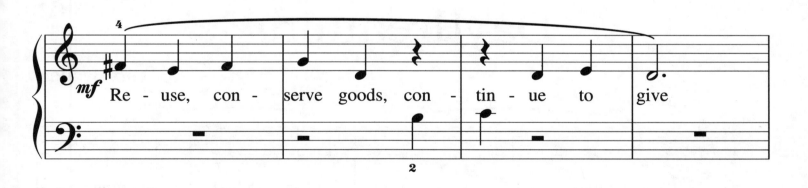

Daydreaming

Lori Bastien

Andante

Some-times while I sit in school, I dream I'm in the swim-ming pool.

Though I work in school all day, I dream of things I'll do when I can play.

The Baby Dinosaur

Lisa Bastien Hanss

Moderato

mf A ba - by di - no - saur came knock - ing at my door. He

asked per - mis - sion for a bite to eat, no more. *f* We

Wrapping Presents

Jane Smisor Bastien

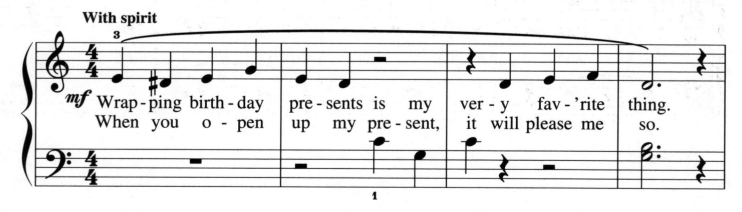

With spirit

mf Wrap-ping birth-day pre-sents is my ver-y fav-'rite thing.
When you o - pen up my pre-sent, it will please me so.

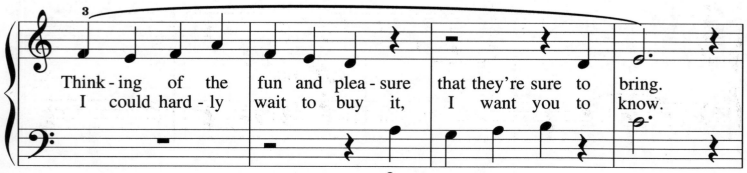

Think-ing of the fun and plea-sure that they're sure to bring.
I could hard-ly wait to buy it, I want you to know.

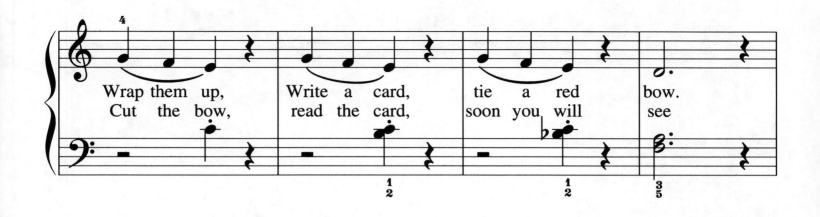

Wrap them up,   Write a card,   tie a red   bow.
Cut the bow,   read the card,   soon you will   see

Soon your birth - day   will be here, You'll   love it   so!
What I got you   for your birth - day.   It's from   me!

Fine

f

D.C. al Fine

ff *rit.*

Night Visitor

Jane Smisor Bastien

Moderato

mf Some - times at night, When I am scared,

I like to turn on the lights.

So I can see Crawl - ing t'ward me

My friend the rol - y pol - y.

8va both hands

Rol - y - pol - y, Do vis - it me,

You are my fav - 'rite night friend!

The Monday Rainbow

Jane Smisor Bastien

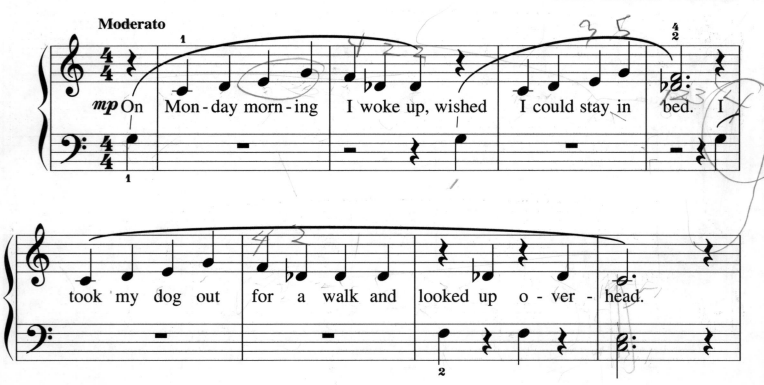

On Mon-day morn-ing I woke up, wished I could stay in bed. I

took my dog out for a walk and looked up o-ver-head.

Roller Blades

Jane Smisor Bastien

Moderato

My dad bought me | rol - ler blades. | They are real - ly | neat.

Ev - 'ry day I | skate a - long | up and down the | street.

A Saturday Date

Lori Bastien

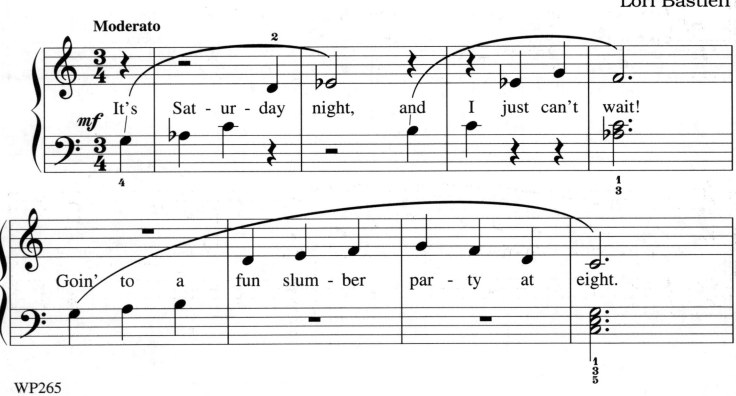

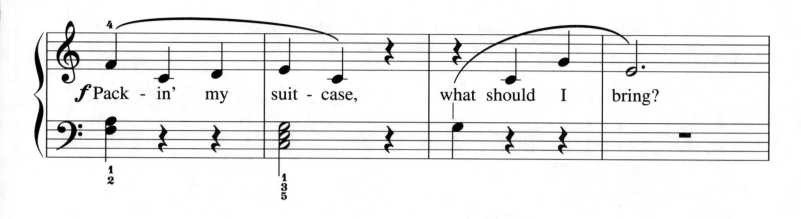

f Pack - in' my suit - case, what should I bring?

Hope that I won't for - get one sin - gle thing.

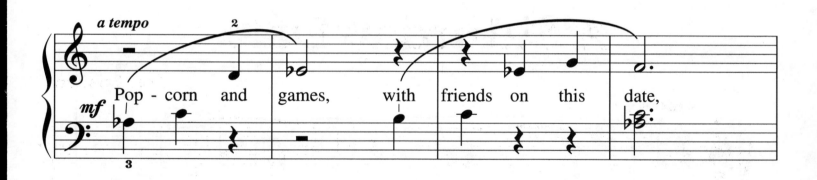

a tempo *mf* Pop - corn and games, with friends on this date,

We'll tell ghost sto - ries and stay up real late. *f* Is - n't it great?

Dancing Ponies

Lori Bastien

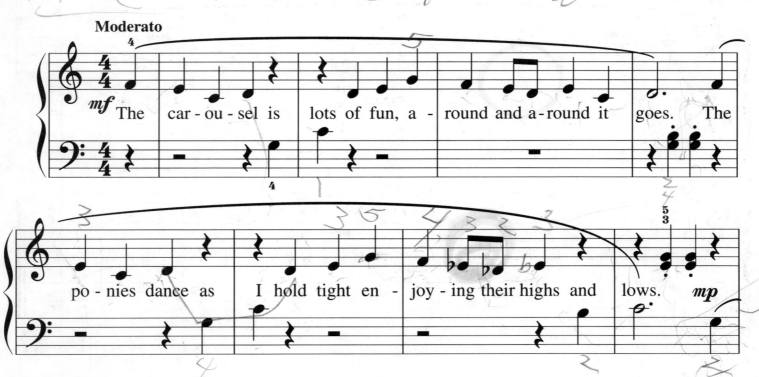

The car-ou-sel is lots of fun, a - round and a-round it goes. The po - nies dance as I hold tight en - joy - ing their highs and lows.

Backyard Friends

Lisa Bastien Hanss

Moderato

mf Out - side my house in a lit - tle flow - ing creek live the back - yard

friends I seek. Frogs, drag - on flies, spi - ders real - ly aren't so meek. I spend time with

them all week! My back - yard friends and I have fun you see.

Parade of the Stars

Jane Smisor Bastien

Moderato

Ev - 'ry night when | it is dark, | Look up in the | sky.

You will see a | spe - cial sight, | As the stars pass | by.

ABOUT THE COMPOSERS

Jane Smisor Bastien

Jane Smisor Bastien and her husband, James, have written many piano books over the years for elementary students. Jane still maintains a full teaching schedule in her home in La Jolla, California.

The Bastiens' writing career began years ago when Jane needed music for her pre-school beginners. Because there wasn't an appropriate method she wrote her own to use with the small class of four- and five-year-old beginners she was teaching. Lisa, their first child, was in that class. By the time their second child Lori was four, Jane's method—*The Very Young Pianist Library* was published.

As Lisa and Lori grew up they witnessed the stream of students who learned in the Bastien home studio. They became teaching assistants at an early age and during their high school (and college) years they had their own students. They spent their high school summers at the National Music Camp in Interlochen, Michigan. Lori later returned as a counselor. During their college summers they enjoyed teaching their mother's students while she was away on workshop tours.

Lisa and Lori are now independent piano teachers and active in their local music teacher organizations.

Lisa Bastien Hanss teaches in the preparatory department at Loyola University and in her home studio in New Orleans, Louisiana. Her Bachelor of Music in Piano Performance/Pedagogy is from Drake University (Des Moines) and her Master of Music in the same area is from Arizona State University. While at ASU Lisa was instrumental in establishing the School of Music's preparatory department.

Lori Bastien established a full class of students in Houston prior to returning to La Jolla, California to do the same. She attended the University of Redlands (California) for two years before transferring to Rice University (Houston) where she received a Bachelor of Music in Piano Performance.